Lost in the jungle

Roderick Hunt   Alex Brychta

Characters

Narrator

Biff

Kipper

Mum/Lady

Chip

Anneena

Man

Casting

This play has seven speaking parts, so that it can be
read aloud in a small group. The longer parts are the
Narrator, Biff, Mum/Lady and Chip, and the shorter
parts are Anneena and the Man.

Scene 1

Narrator Scene 1 'A present for Mum'
It was Mum's birthday.
Chip had a box of chocolates for her.
Kipper made her a little monkey, but
Biff didn't know what to get.

Biff I don't know what to get Mum.
Perhaps I'll get her a plant.

Narrator   Biff asked Anneena's Mum to help her.
They went to a garden centre.
There was a greenhouse full of plants.

Biff   It's like a jungle in here.
There are so many plants.
I don't know which one to buy.
Oh. This is the one I like.
I'll get this one for Mum.

Scene 2

Narrator   Scene 2 'Mum's birthday'

Children   *(together)* Happy birthday, Mum.

Kipper   Open my present first.

(Sound of paper as Mum opens her presents)

Mum   It's a little monkey.

Biff I think it looks like Kipper.

Kipper Oh no it doesn't!

Mum Well I think it's lovely.

Chip Open my present next.

Mum Oh good! Chocolates!
Thank you, Chip.

Biff Here's my present.

Mum Oh, thank you!
What a lovely plant, Biff.

Narrator Dad had a present for Mum.
It was a plant, too.

Mum Another plant!
I don't mind a bit!

Narrator Anneena came round to play.

Anneena This is from my Mum.
Happy birthday.

Mum What a lovely plant! Thank you.

Narrator Then Wilma's mum came round.
She had a plant, too.

Mum Thank you. I love plants.
It's quite like a jungle in here.

Scene 3

Narrator Scene 3 'The magic key glows'
The children went to Biff's room.
Anneena looked at the little house.

Anneena I love this little house.
Can we have a magic adventure?

Kipper We can if the key glows.

Anneena Look! The key is glowing.

(Sound of magic working)

Chip We're in a jungle.
Look at all these plants.

Biff It's wonderful. Look at that one.
It's ten times bigger than
the one I gave Mum.

(Sound of monkey chattering in a tree)

Anneena There's a monkey jumping up and down on a branch.

Kipper It looks cross.
I don't think it likes us.

Chip It looks like you.

(Sound of monkey chattering angrily)

Anneena   It's getting angry.

Chip   Oh no! It's throwing things at us.

Biff   We can't stay here. Come on.

Narrator The children ran through the jungle.
Suddenly, Chip stopped.
There was a big snake in the way.

Chip Oh no! Look at this snake.
We can't go this way. Come on.

Narrator   They came to a river.
There were alligators asleep on
the bank.

Kipper   Don't wake them up.
They might get angry.

Biff   They might like you for dinner.

Narrator Suddenly they fell into a big net.
It pulled them up in the air.

(Sound of net being pulled up)

Anneena Oh help! We're in a trap.

Chip It's a trap to catch animals.

Children *(together)* Help! Help!

Kipper Let us down.

Narrator A man and a lady came out of the trees.

Chip Look. There's a man and a lady.

Man We're explorers.

Lady Don't worry.
We'll soon get you down.

Narrator The explorers took the children to their camp.

Man What are you doing in the jungle? Are you lost?

Biff Yes. I think we are.

Lady So are we. But then, we have been lost for years.
We are looking for a place called the Lost City.

Anneena Maybe we can help you find it.

Kipper Maybe we can find it today.

Man I don't think so.
We have been looking for years.

Scene 4

Narrator   Scene 4 'The search for the
Lost City'
They set out to find the Lost City.
They came to a rope bridge.

Biff   Maybe the Lost City is over there.
Come on. Let's go and see.

Kipper   I hope this bridge is safe.
It looks a long way to fall.

Narrator After a time they came to a river.
They found a boat.

Lady Oh good. We lost this boat years ago.

Man Get in everyone.
We'll paddle down the river.

(Sound of paddling and rippling water)

Chip Look at the alligators.
I hope it's not their dinner time.

(Sound of roaring waterfall)

Lady Look! A waterfall!

Man Look out! The paddle has broken.
We're going through the waterfall.
We're going to get wet.

Anneena Oh! I don't like getting wet.

Chip Think of the alligators.
It's better than being eaten.

Narrator Behind the waterfall were some steps.

Lady This may be the way to the Lost City.

Narrator At last they came to the top of the steps.

Man It's the Lost City!

Kipper I knew we'd find it today.

Lady Nobody has been here for years.

Man   Help me open this door.

(Sound of door opening)

Anneena   What a wonderful place.
There's gold everywhere.

Chip   Look! Everything is made of gold.

Biff   There's a gold throne.

Biff Look at that monkey behind Kipper.

Chip Which one is the monkey?

Kipper The key is glowing.
It's time to go home.

Lady Goodbye. Thank you for helping us.

Man I wish we had a magic key.

(Sound of magic working)

Scene 5

Narrator Scene 5 'The adventure ends'

Anneena That was a good adventure.

Biff Here's a plant from the Lost City.
I'll put it in Mum's jungle.

Chip I know where we can get a monkey, too.

Kipper That's *not* funny, Chip.